Color-Ado

Presents to you

A Forbidden Cheese Coloring Book!

Also available:

Forbidden Cheese
Read-Aloud

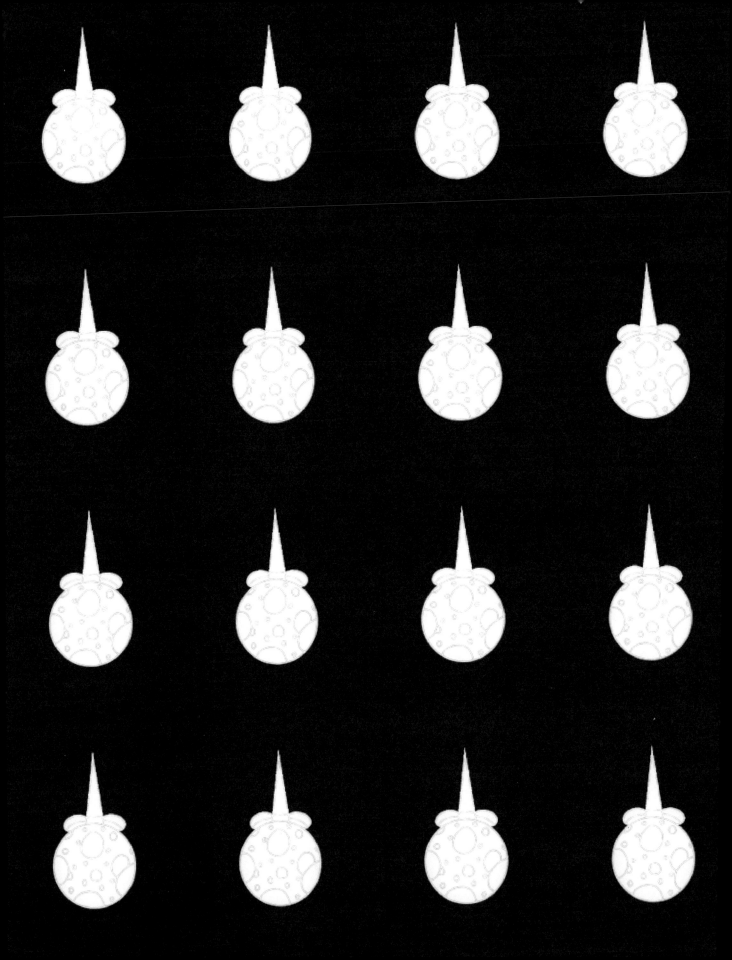

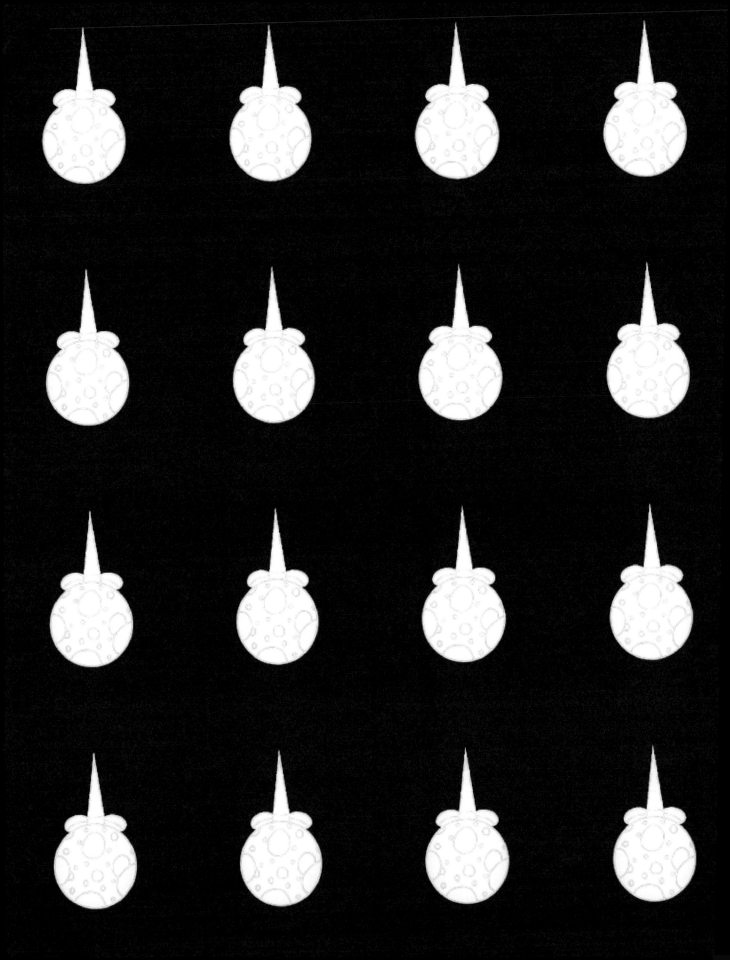

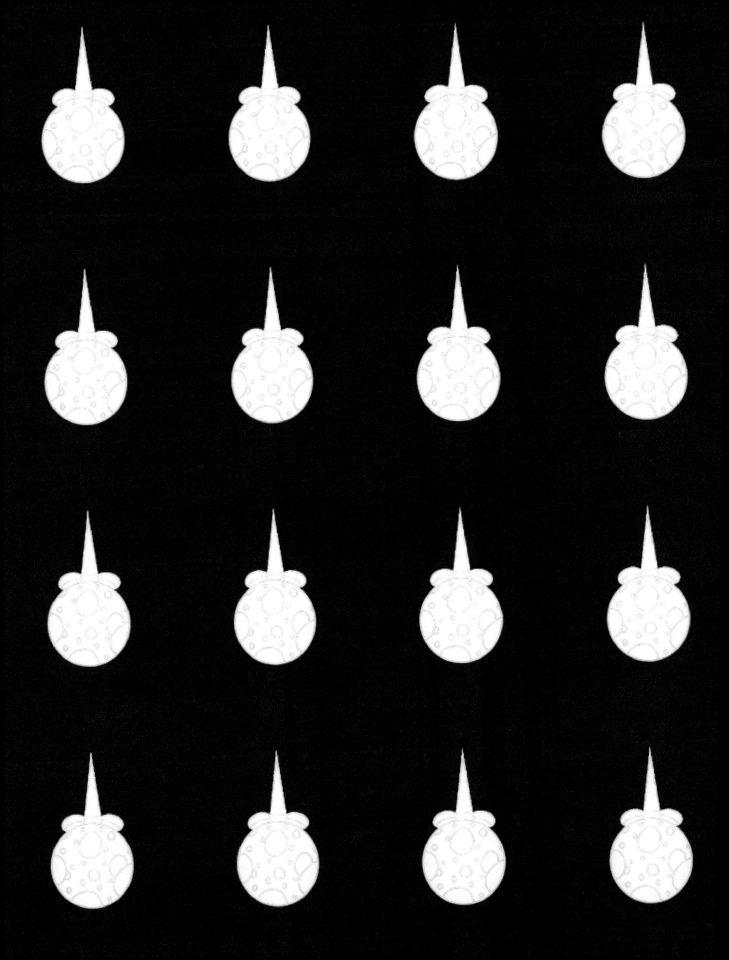

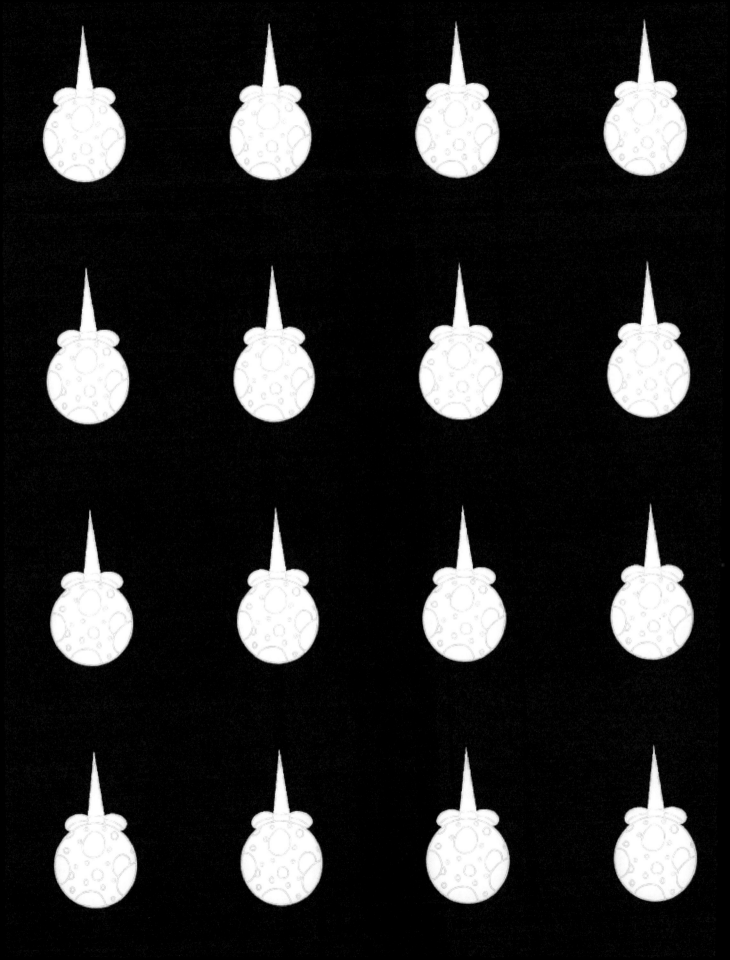

Dot-2-Dot

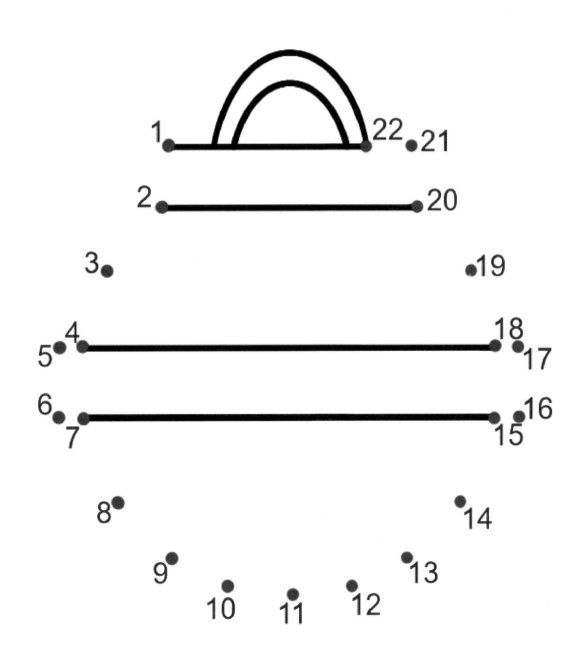

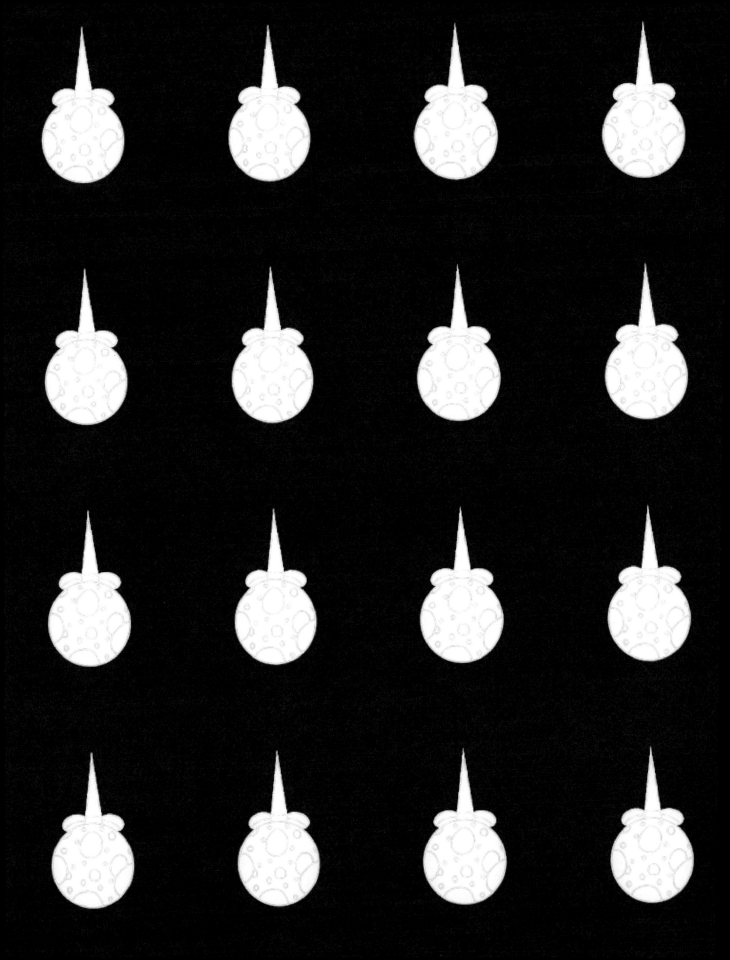

Count the Cheese!

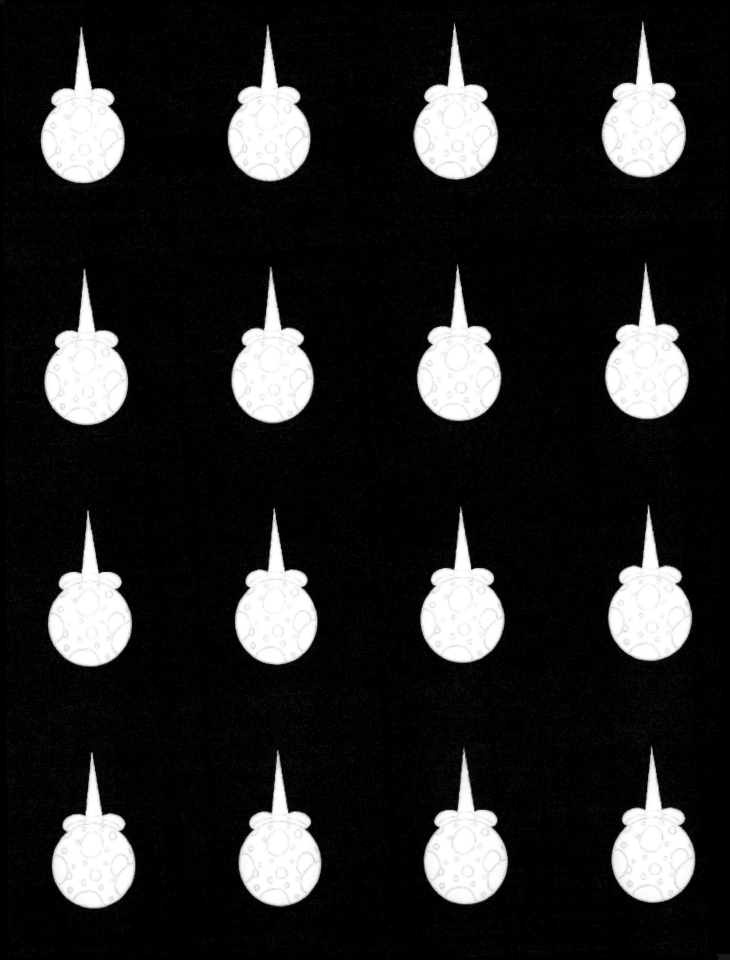

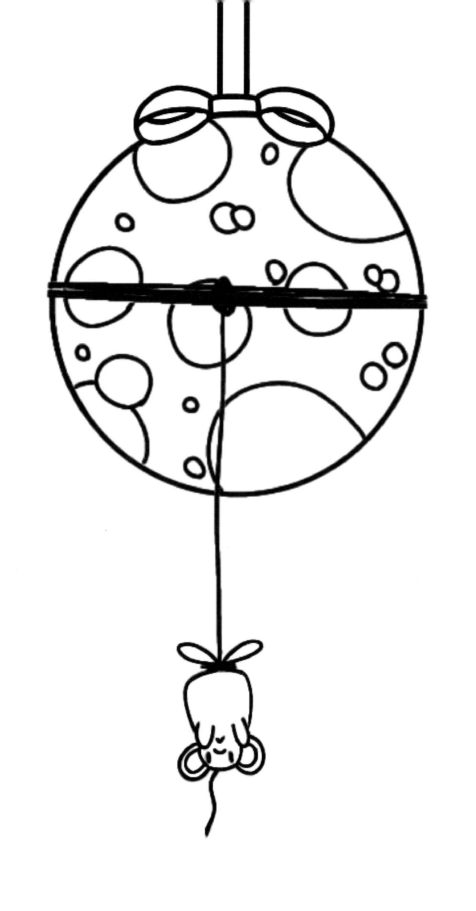

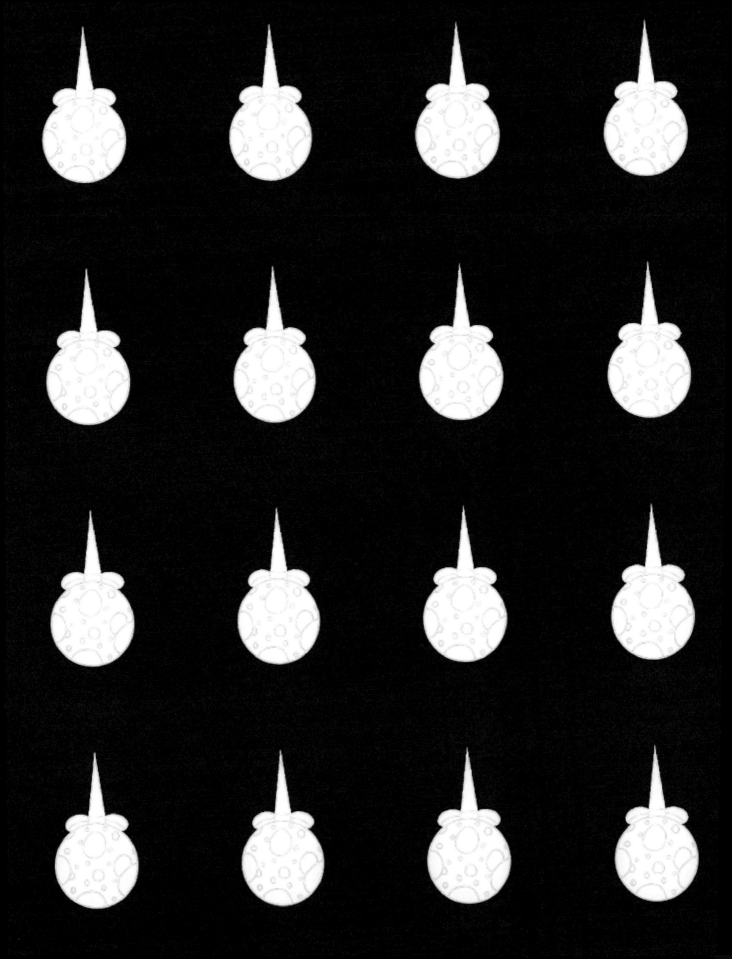

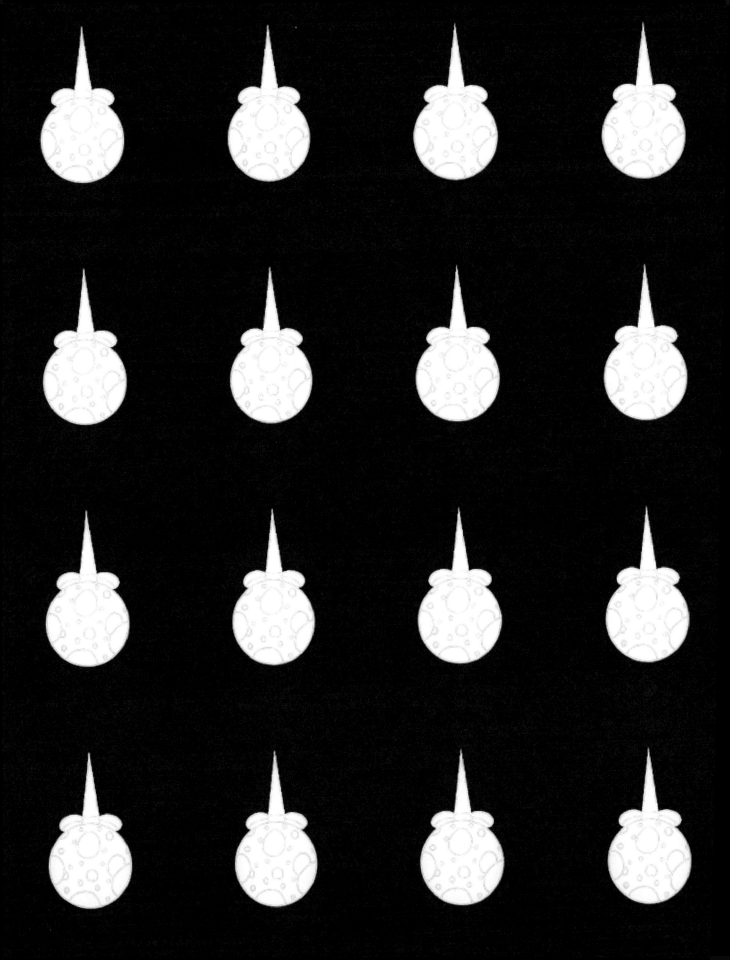

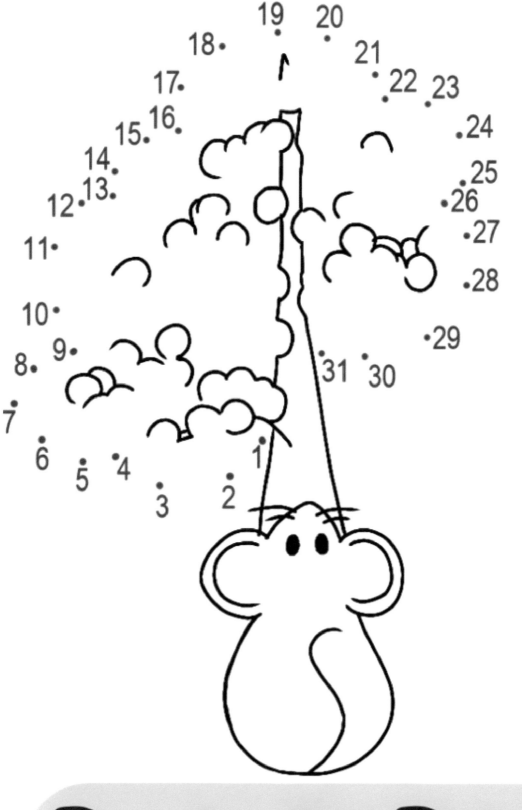

Dot-2-Dot

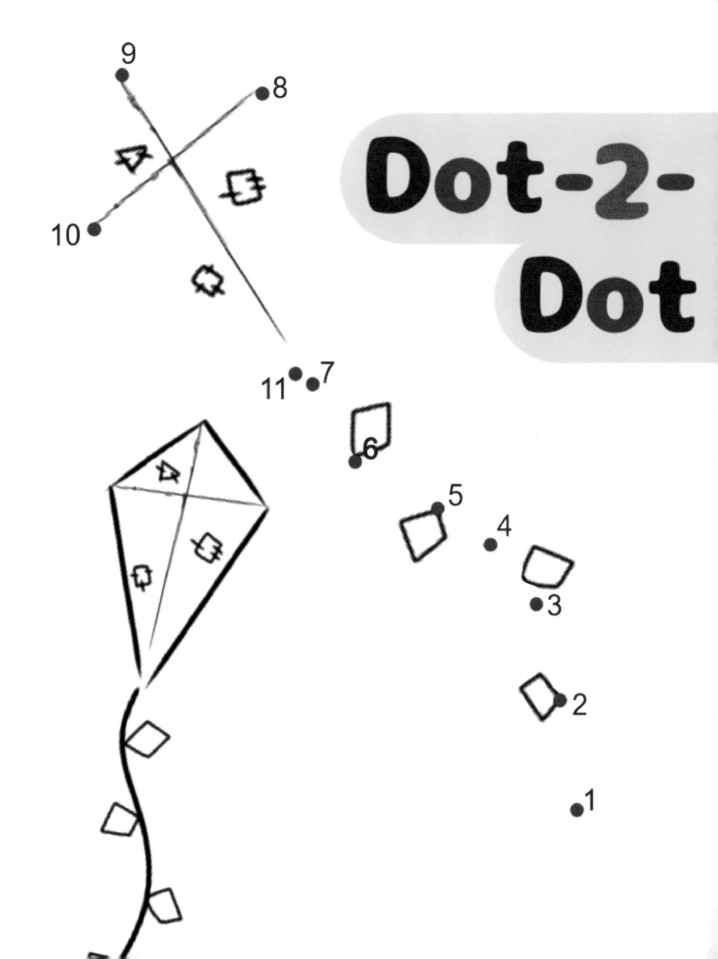

Dot-2-Dot

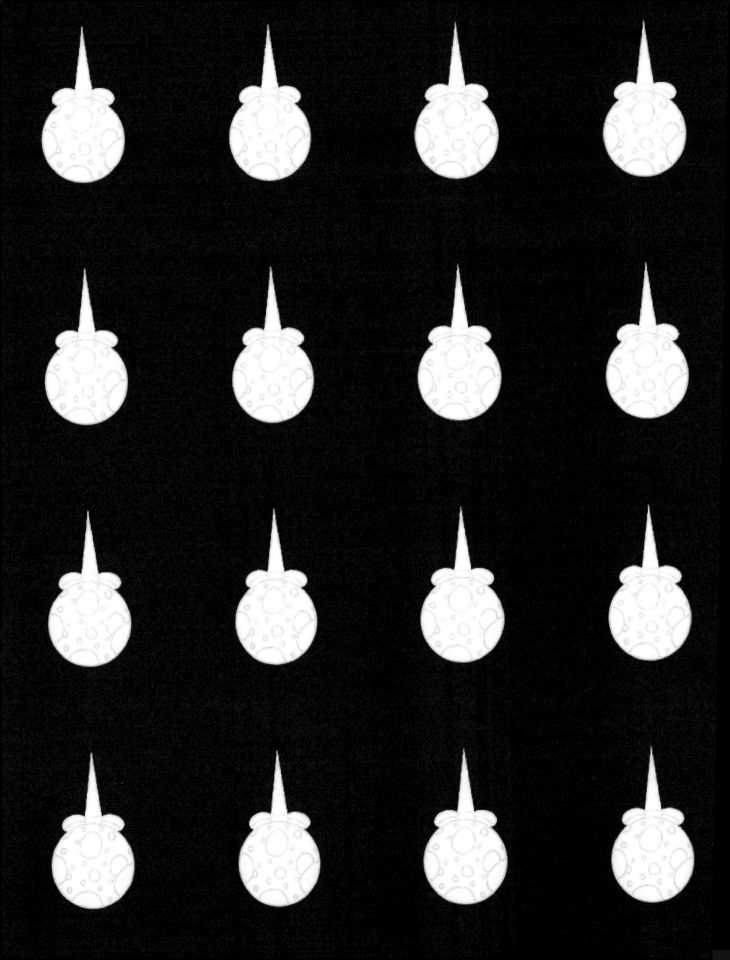

Dot-2-Dot

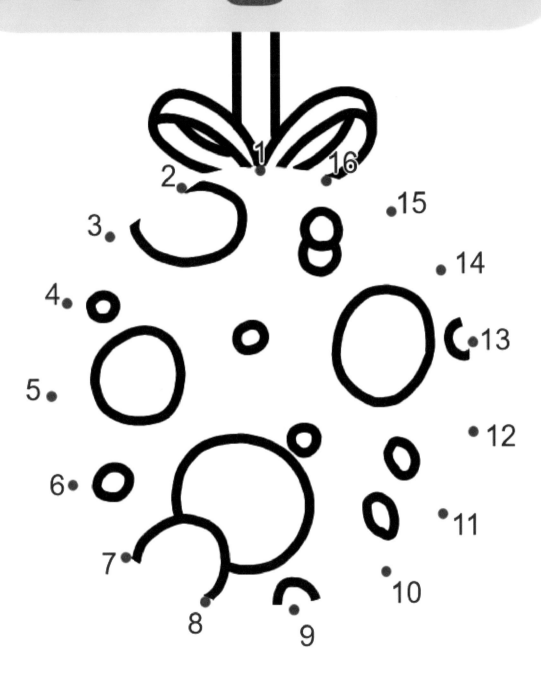

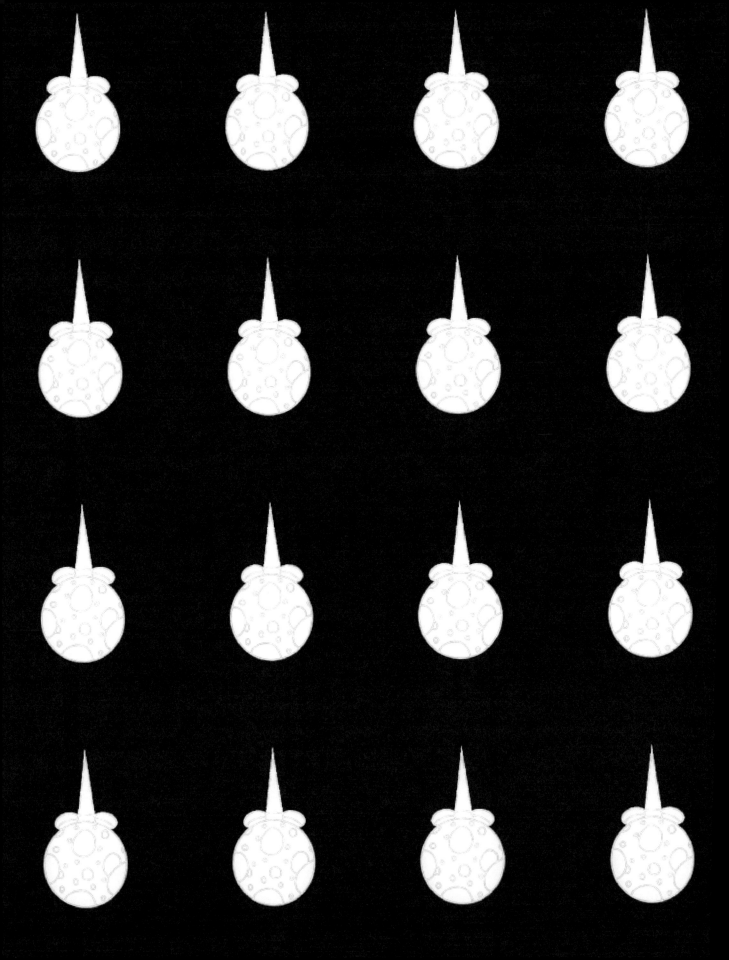

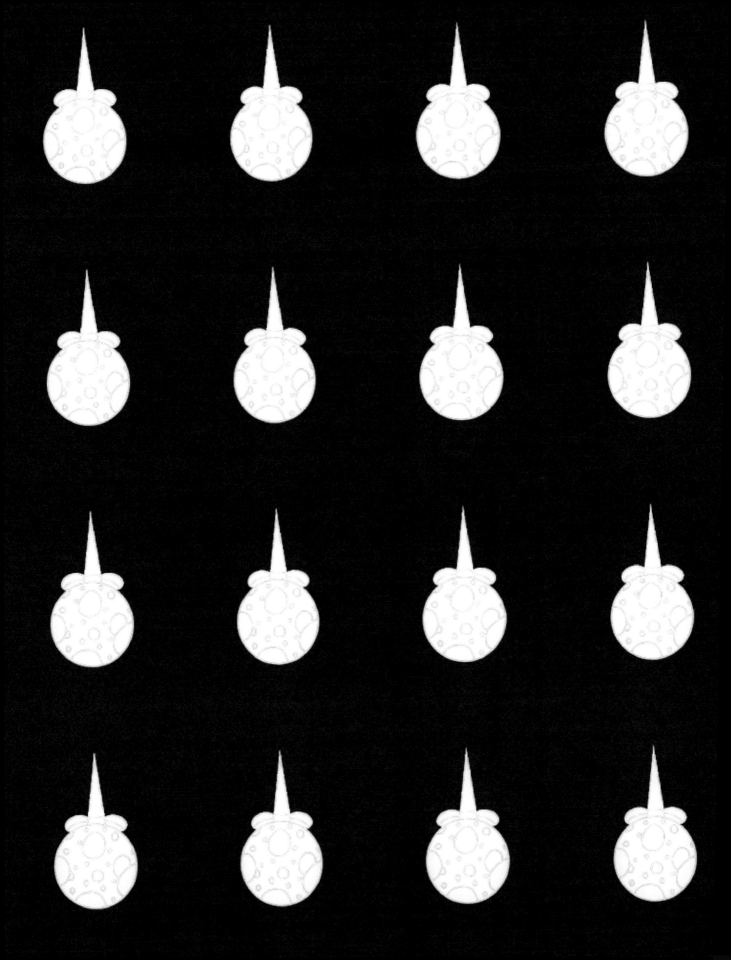

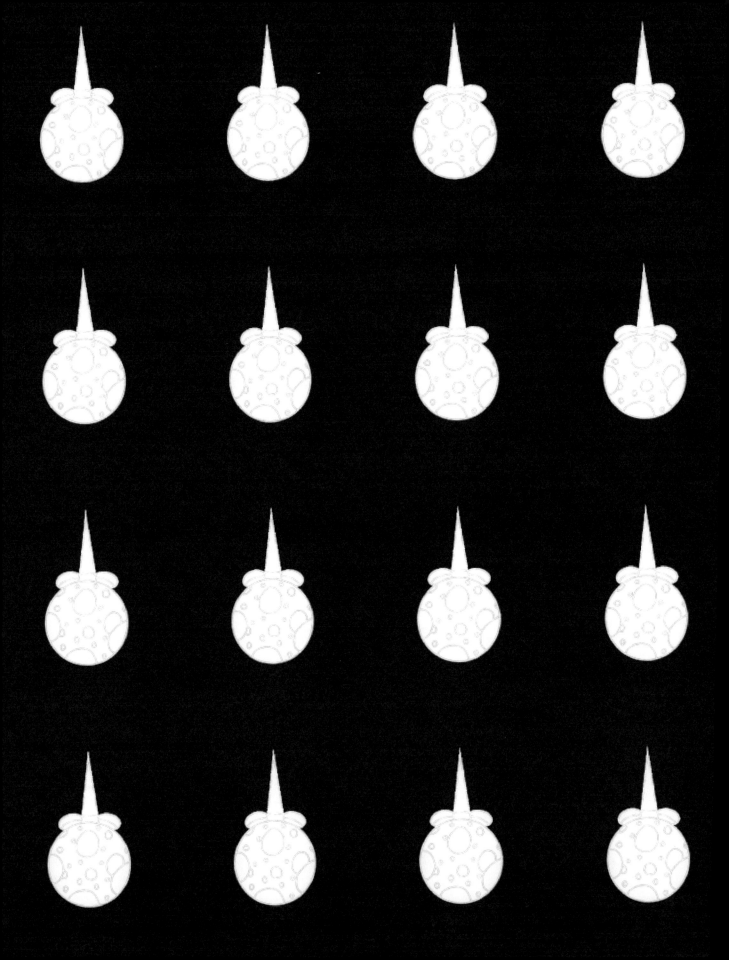

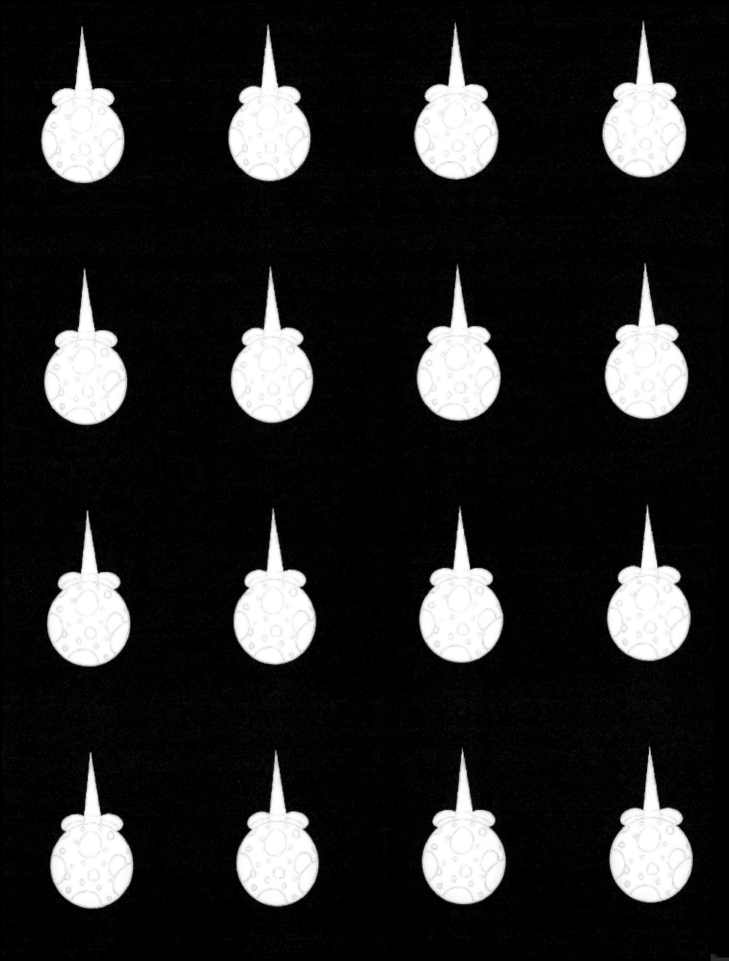

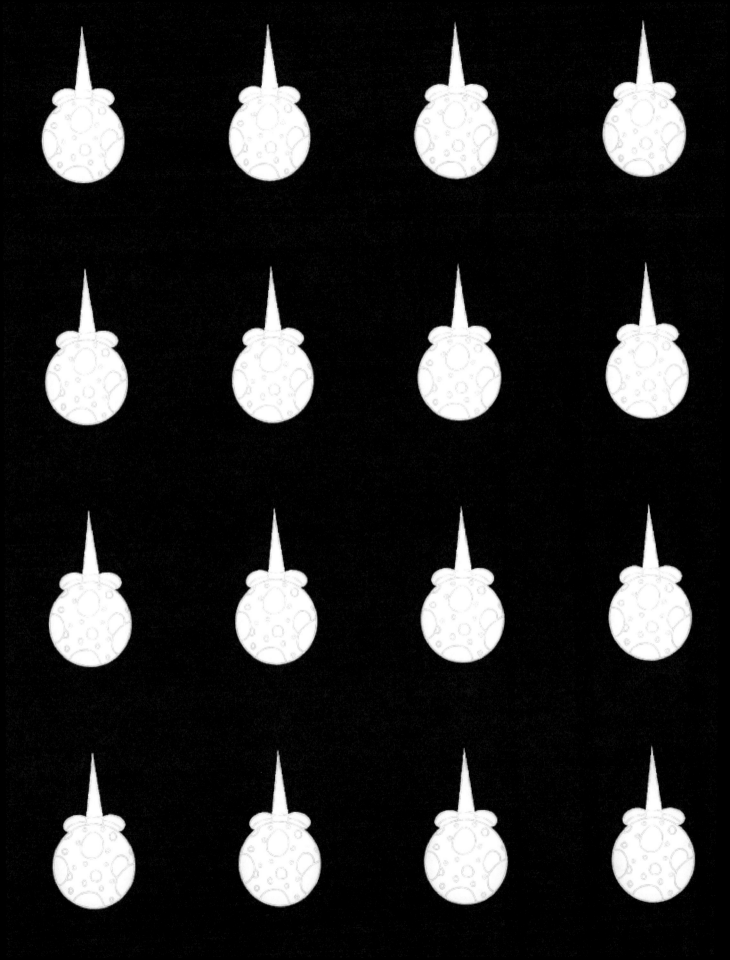

Dot-2-Dot

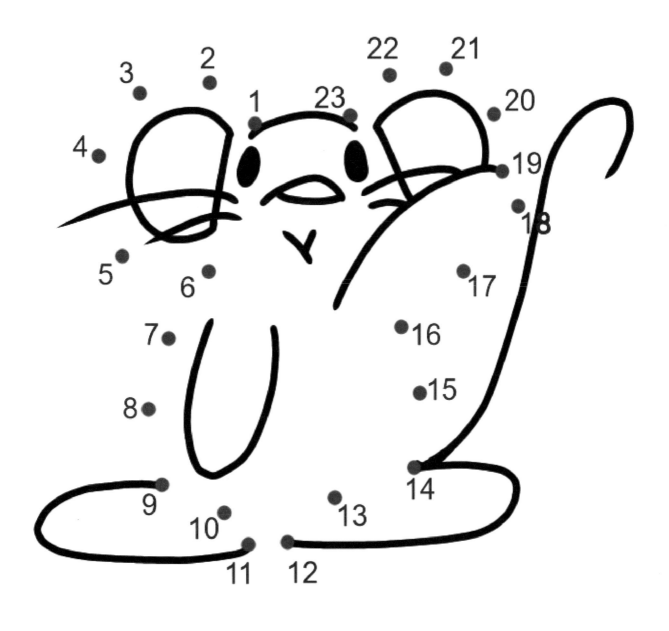

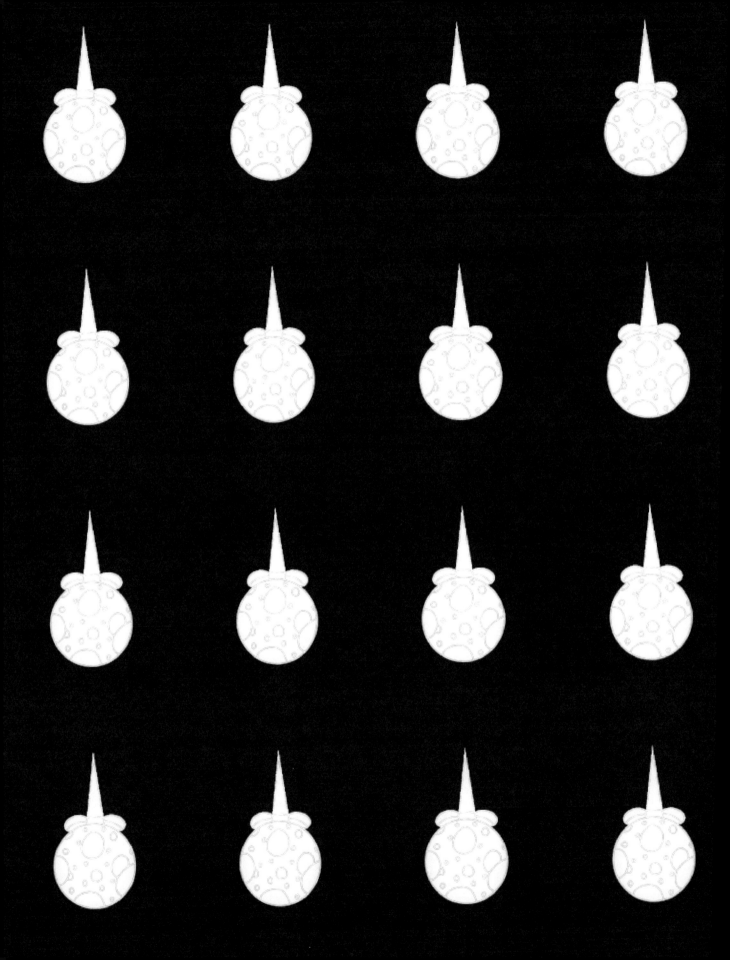

Made in United States
Troutdale, OR
12/09/2024

26183145R00033